Books by Boxer:
Swinnow Lane, Bramley,
Leeds, UK LS13 4BS

Tel: 01133 955 593
Fax: 01133 955 594
email: sales@booksbyboxer.com
Web: www.booksbyboxer.com

C000154838

ISBN 9781909732087
Item Code: YOA0005

Printed and bound in China

# LOVE & PASSION FOR THE ELDERLY

## BY THE
## SILVEY JEX PARTNERSHIP

HELLO HANDSOME !

ARE YOU FOLLOWING ME YOUNG MAN?

SIGH! BY THE TIME WE'VE GOT OUR CLOTHES OFF, THE MOOD WILL HAVE GONE!

YES IT'S VERY NICE MR POTTER...NOW WHAT'S THIS ABOUT AN INGROWING TOE NAIL?

YOU'RE SUPPOSED TO GO TO SLEEP AFTER IT...NOT DURING IT!

YO SWEET SISTERS—EVERYTHING'S COOL. WHICH BABE'S GONNA
CHECK OUT WITH SUPER STUD AND GIT ON DOWN TO MY LOVE THANG!

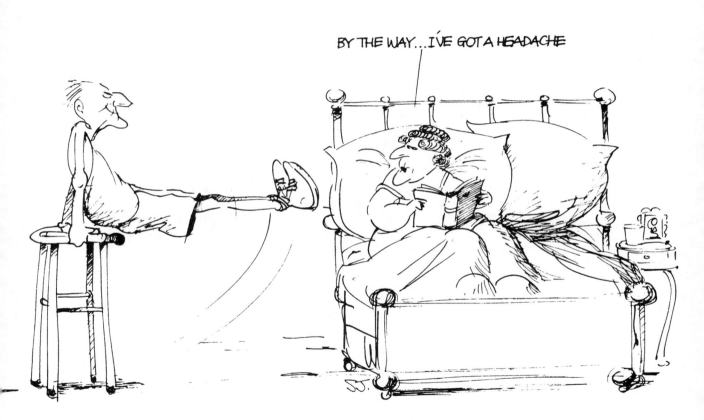

I'M TINGLING WITH EXCITEMENT—OR IT COULD BE MY POOR CIRCULATION

IT'S ALRIGHT OLD GIRL ... I'M WEARING A CATHETER

IT'S LOVELY HERBERT — JUST WHAT I'VE ALWAYS WANTED

WHY CAN'T YOU SLEEP AFTER LUNCH LIKE <u>OTHER</u> OLD MEN?

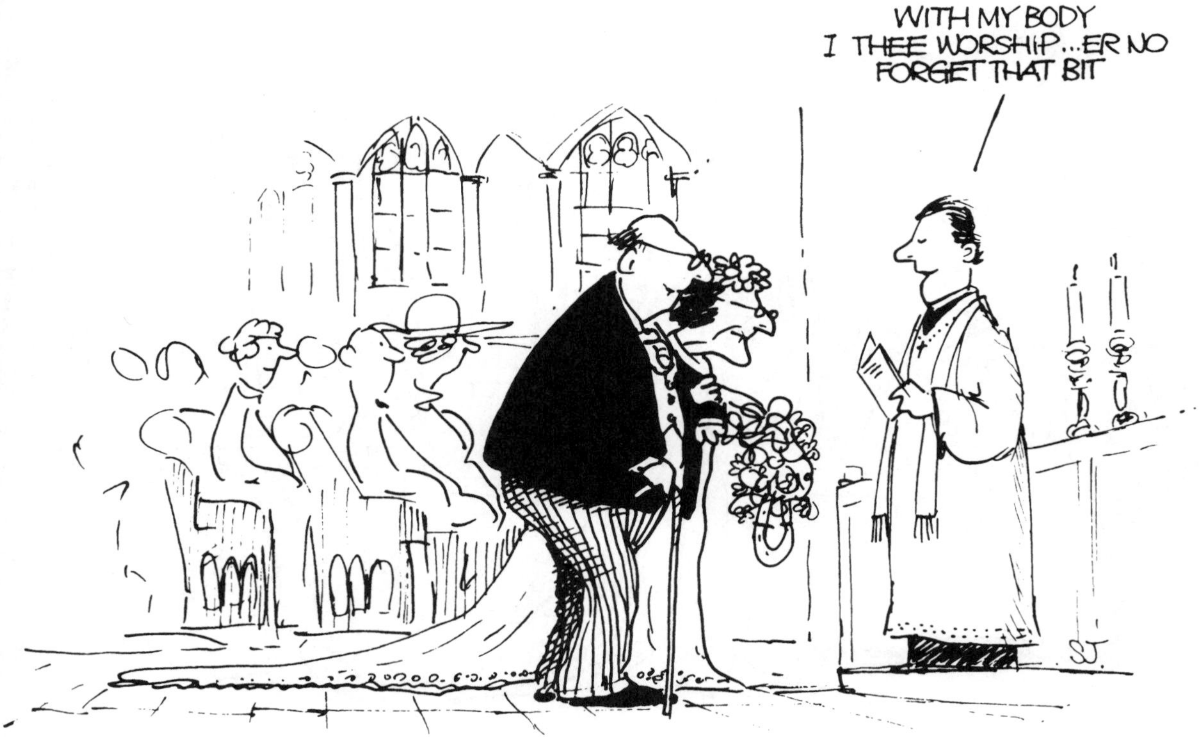
WITH MY BODY
I THEE WORSHIP...ER NO
FORGET THAT BIT
SJ.

...I HOPE YOU'RE READY FOR THIS MY DEAR...
I'VE GOT SOME JUMP LEADS ATTACHED TO THE YOUNG MAN NEXT DOOR

OH MR MARCO YOU SEXY BEAST—
LET'S GO BACK TO MY PLACE AFTER THE SHOW AND MAKE LOVE

TYING ME TO THE BED IS OKAY... BUT DID YOU <u>HAVE</u> TO USE A GRANNY KNOT?

FUNNY... WHEN I WAS YOUNG I ALWAYS FANCIED AN OLDER MAN...BUT NOW...

NO, NO—I SAID...I'VE GOT ACUTE <u>ANGINA</u> !!

AFTER YOU WITH THE TEETH, MY DARLING

STAY DOWN THERE MISS WILKINS, I THINK I HEAR MATRON COMING

...AND LOOK AT THE SHODDY CRAFTSMANSHIP ON THESE...
THEY'VE FORGOTTEN TO STITCH THE CROTCH UP.

DON'T LOOK DEAR....THEY'LL ONLY GET SILLY

IF YOU'RE FREE...I'M FREE AND I MEAN <u>FREE</u>

I'D BETTER NOT GO DOWN . . . . I WON'T BE ABLE TO GET UP AGAIN

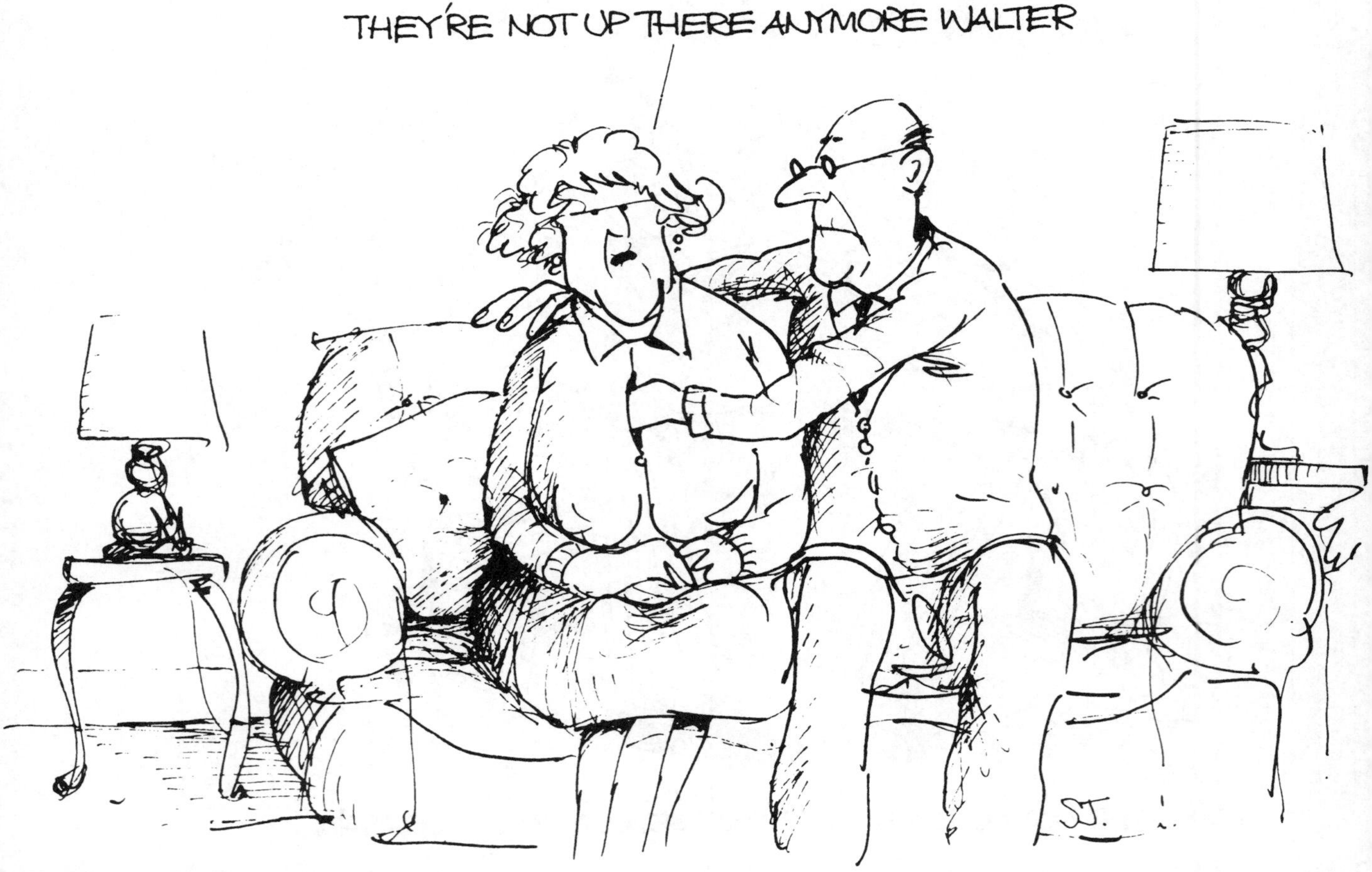
THEY'RE NOT UP THERE ANYMORE WALTER
SJ.

YOUR PERFUME IS DRIVING ME CRAZY... DEEP HEAT WAS ALWAYS MY FAVOURITE

ARE YOU GIRLS INTERESTED IN A GAME OF STRIP CRIBBAGE?

I SAID...OOH..AHH...YES..YES..OOH DON'T STOP...YES...YES..

PHEW! THESE RUBBER SHEETS GENERATE SOME HEAT DON'T THEY?

FOR GOD'S SAKE WOMAN GET OFF ME

WHAT WOULD YOU CHARGE FOR FIVE MINUTES LAP DANCING?

LOOK EVERYBODY - IT'S GEORGE BACK FROM HIS LITTLE TRANSPLANT OPERATION

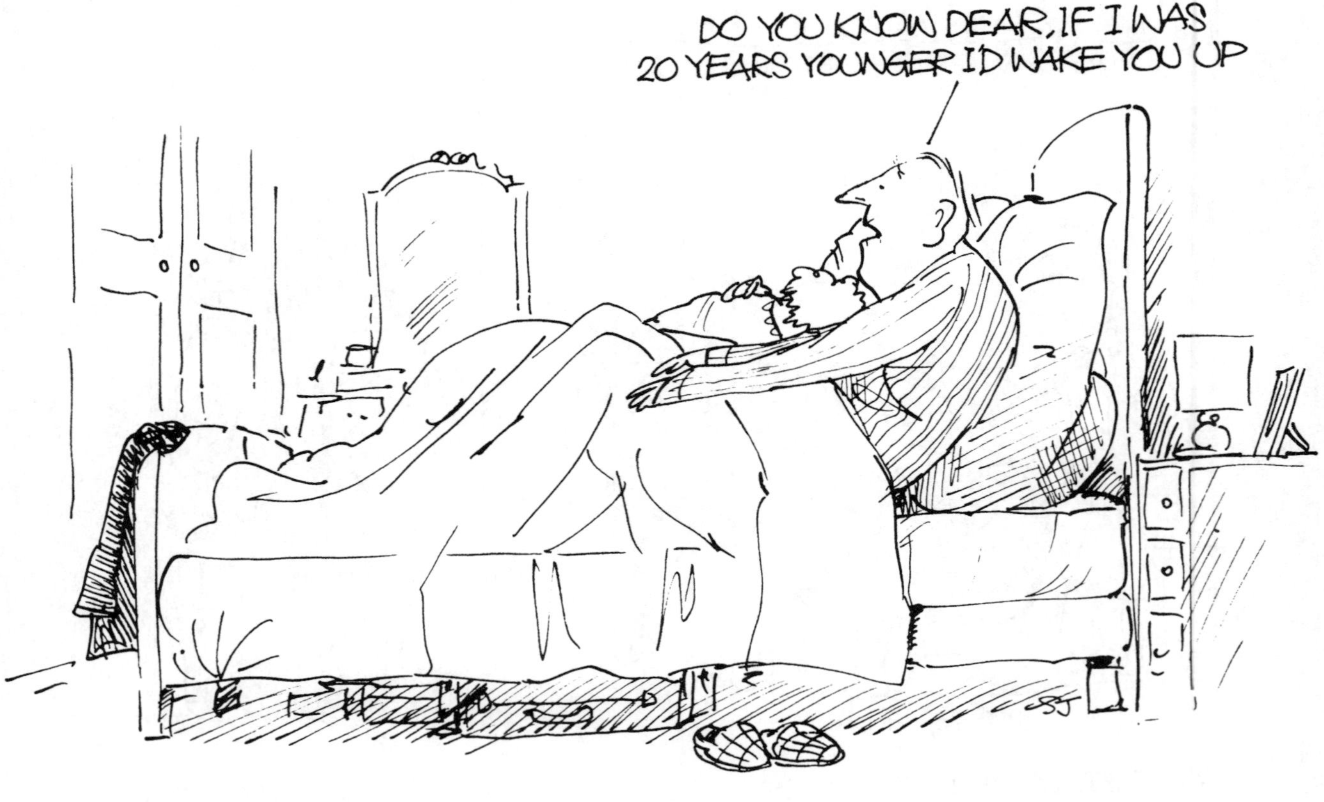
DO YOU KNOW DEAR, IF I WAS
20 YEARS YOUNGER I'D WAKE YOU UP

WHAT DO YOU SAY WE POOL OUR PENSIONS AND GET A HOTEL ROOM?

# OTHER GREAT TITLES FROM Books By Boxer

The fine cultivated shops carrying our titles really do get ticked off if you buy direct from the publisher so, if you can, please patronise your local g
and card shop and let them make a bob or two. If however, the fools don't carry a particular title, you can order them from us.

## LITTLE PAPERBACKS: RRP £2.99 to £3.50

## FUN MINTS: RRP £1.99

 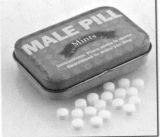 

Books by Boxer:
Swinnow Lane, Bramley,
Leeds, UK LS13 4BS

Tel: 01133 955 593
Fax: 01133 955 594
email: sales@booksbyboxer.cc
Web: www.booksbyboxer.con

You can order other Little books directly from Books by Boxer.